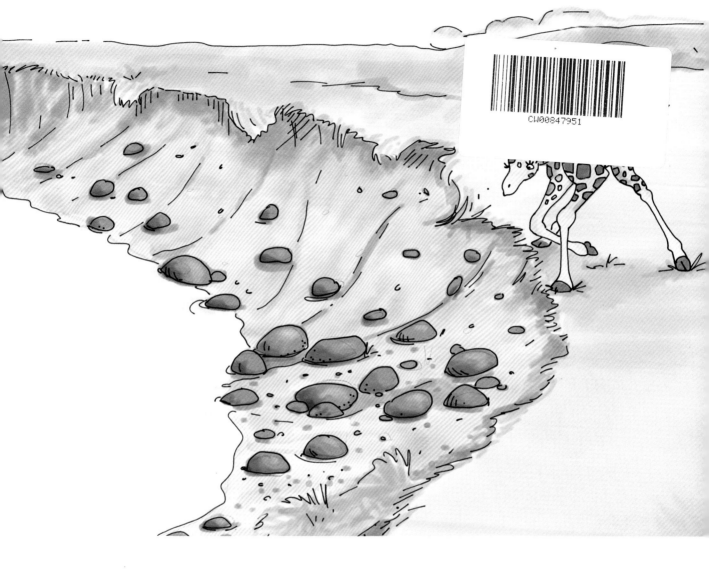

One day Alfie and Harpo see a little giraffe on the bank of the river.

1

She is thirsty. Alfie and Harpo help her
get down to the river.

The little giraffe goes into the river.

She has a drink of water.

Then she turns round to come out of the water, but she slips and falls.

The little giraffe tries to stand up, but she cannot get back on her feet.

Alfie and Harpo pull and push her until
she can stand on her feet again.

Then they help her get out of the river
and go up the riverbank.

'Thank you,' says the little giraffe. She runs back to her family by the trees.